Library of Congress Control Number: 2008903852
Blum, Joseph Emil
The Sawmill Ballroom Lavender Farm Guide to Growing Lavender / Joseph Emil Blum.
Eugene, Oregon: Sawmill Ballroom Publishing, 2008
p. cm.
Includes index.
Trade Paperback
ISBN 9780979981616

Cover and content design by Chrissy Richards, Lightbox Graphic Design

THE SAWMILL BALLROOM LAVENDER FARM

GUIDE TO GROWING

Lavender

SECOND EDITION

PRACTICAL GUIDELINES FOR THE SUCCESSFUL CULTIVATION,
PROPAGATION AND UTILIZATION OF LAVENDER

BY JOSEPH EMIL BLUM

©2008

Table of Contents

Section Four: After the Harvest

There is land that hands of humans have touched and that still breathes with life. There is land that speaks in silences, winds breathing, water trickling, seeping, gathering color. There is land that sleeps under the sky and speaks with the moon about the sun, then the sun about the moon. People, like gnats, think they can preside over these things. All the forces are laughing at them.

⌈⌉

The Coyote Dance

The Ballroom is holding the Coyote Dance

for all the spirits that run across the highway into the field

where the farmer turns his tractor to the dry pasture

Sees coyote

Thinks, should he jump down, run to the shed, grab his gun

Thinks again

Watches as Coyote runs oblivious to the barbed wire boundary

with abandon, tongue hanging out running through the air so fast

flat out, burners kicking with freedom

dust spots floating above where his paws touch the ground

almost invisible until he reaches the pines

by the rocks above the dusty field

Then the farmer looks down at his watch

tick, tick, ticking something he calls time

Something Coyote feels in his blood

as he disappears into the pines

© Joey Emil Blum 1988

The Coyote Dance holds the origin of the name, Sawmill Ballroom

1

Dedicated to Nancy, Ruby, Ilsa, and Sasha who skillfully took cuttings,
stuck plugs, hauled mulch, sifted flowers, weeded, watered, arranged, rearranged,
lifted pots, filled pots, under the sun and in the rain all that allowed me to
write this book with a deeper knowledge of what it takes to grow plants.

Let it at least be said we had some fun.

I would also like to dedicate this book to the patience and certainty
that earth, wind, and fire have taught me.

PREFACE TO THE SECOND EDITION

It is eight years since the first edition of this book. Since then I have spoken with scores and scores of lavender growers, and those wanting to become lavender growers, from Europe, Asia, Australia, South and North America about growing lavender. In that time a lot has changed in the commercial world of lavender. An industry that was centered in Provence, France, has now spread across the globe. What started as a possibility, then developed into a fad, and rapidly escalated into a trend, has now settled once again into a possibility. There is more demand than ever for lavender, but there is now also more supply than ever. And thankfully, the wave of get-rich-quick delusion that followed *Forbes Magazine* running a small article about a couple who "hoped" to make $500,000 a year on their five acres of lavender has passed. The inundation of people wanting to "get into the game" has likewise passed, as few became rich, many got in, then out, and most have learned that lavender is a lovely flower, not a precious metal.

Thankfully as well, those considering growing lavender can now do so with a less feverish approach: one that is rooted in common sense and thoughtful consideration of a few basic principles, instead of the numbers crunchers and technical data junkies who flooded the market blinded by dollar signs, oil recovery coefficients, and value added pipe dreams. I am not trying to disparage technical information, some of it is useful, but most of the "studies" and "feasibility assessments" did not address the fundamental requirements of growing the plant. Until you know how to grow the plant, what good is all that potential? With that said, you will not find the specific gravity of the oil of a particular cultivar of lavender in this book, nor will you find endless lists of hard-to-find cultivars offering the promise of the secret oils of the Himalayas, Andes, Alps, or ancient Rome. You can find most of that on the Internet, although a lot of it won't be accurate and will distract you from what you need to do to be a capable lavender grower. Growing things successfully still comes down to your love, devotion, and enthusiasm for what you're doing.

Since the first edition came out, more than a few people have asked for some more about this, or a little more about that, or I'm not sure what you meant by that. The thing most readers wanted to know more about was propagation; I've tried to answer these questions in this edition. Also, I have added more about fertilizing, watering, and the seasonal behavior of plants, plus an odd tip here and there from our own experience, which, now that I have likely passed the half-way point of my life, I feel less inclined to hold close, more ready to reveal.

The first edition of this book, I believe, helped a lot of people. Only one buyer returned the first edition, and I suspect she read it first, took her money's worth, and then demanded a refund. That's the old joke about a restaurant patron who summons the waiter to complain about the food, "Waiter, this food is awful! You have to take it back." "Certainly, Madam," the waiter replies, "but perhaps you might return it before you finish next time." I hope this is a better, more useful book. Let me know what you think.

ɢʒ

INTRODUCTION

The Sawmill Ballroom Lavender Farm began growing lavender almost 21 years ago. We did not sit down and decide to start a lavender business, nor did we do exhaustive agricultural or market research: we just started growing lavender because Nancy loved it, we needed a source of income, and we wanted something in abundance. That something became lavender.

Our nursery began in a garden in Lucca, Italy, where Milena, a kind "friend of a friend" welcomed us to her house; she walked us upstairs to our room where, on the bed, was a lovely pillow stuffed with lavender. Nancy was in heaven. Lavender had long been one of her favorite plants and to be in a two-hundred-year-old stone house, surrounded by the charm that is Tuscany, with a lavender-stuffed pillow adorning a beautiful bed—well, it was great. When we squeezed the pillow, the sweetest fragrance wafted into the air. When Nancy asked Milena where the lavender came from, our host pointed out the window to her garden where we saw a row of plants in the tattered state of winter form. Eight days later we left Tuscany with a dozen cuttings from those plants safely tucked into a moist paper towel in a plastic bag. Those cuttings traveled with us through Italy for another two weeks before we returned to Seattle.

Nancy stuck those cuttings in the ground of our vegetable garden in West Seattle; by April most of them had rooted. They grew into the most beautiful, well-formed, and sweet-smelling plants. As they matured, we took more cuttings, and now the plants were growing not only in our front yard, but in friends' yards as well. They withstood Seattle's rains, as well as two weeks of ten-degree freezing, and they always looked beautiful. When we moved to Lorane,
Oregon, we planted them in the soil we sarcastically dubbed "Ham Road Adobe." That Tuscan™ lavender has changed our lives. It has brought many thousands of people great joy, and, though we now grow many more varieties of lavender, we owe a great debt of thanks to our favorite: Tuscan.

☙

Our Farm Today

A lot of people come to our farm. Mostly they come to walk and touch lavender and see the gardens Nancy has created. Many come to buy plants, some to catch tadpoles, some to play with our donkeys. Some, naturally, come and, upon seeing the beauty of the place, start up the fantasy machine (I do it a lot myself when I visit boat-builders and painters' studios). It seems to be human to go somewhere and see the possibility of another way to live.

In an increasingly developed and technological world, our farm is something of a throwback. The Sawmill Ballroom is a simple place. Our small and modest house sits amid the grounds, and the only thing that shouts "modern" is the orange Kubota tractor. We're also a bucolic twenty-mile drive from Eugene, and this distance allows drivers to slow down, breathe, and contemplate en route to our farm. In an hour's visit they see the beauty, the apple trees, the open lawn, and thousands of lavender in bloom. By the time the visit is half over the fantasy mind is churning away and they start thinking, "Maybe I could do this." And they can. But what they don't see is the thousands of hours of year-round work that go into crafting our grounds. That's the way it should be—when you visit someplace it should relax and enchant you. However, if you're reading this book, you've decided to take your interest a step further, and so it is my goal to help you do so without making costly mistakes, either of time or money. I want you to fulfill your dream.

We are very practical people. We also share a great trust that experience is the greatest teacher. You can read books, you can talk to people, you can search the Internet, you can assay, soil sample, and gather data until your eyes pop out of your head, but doing something yourself will usually lead you to what you need to know. After years of growing lavender, we're beginning to understand all those things we read before but that didn't mean anything to us when we started. Now we have something to enrich and enlighten other growers' experiences—namely, our own experience. That is what this book is all about. This book tells you what we've been through, how we think, and how we successfully grow and propagate beautiful lavender plants in the Pacific Northwest. I try not to make any claims about things of which I have no first-hand experience. This means I cannot answer questions here about growing in the tropics or exact rates of oil extraction for the now abundant varieties of lavender being grown worldwide. I trust that this book will give you the encouragement and real-world experience necessary to have a go at this wonderful undertaking.

Whether for personal enjoyment, as a commercial crop for the floral, oil, or specialty market trade, or as the centerpiece of a winery, eco-recreation destination, or large or small landscape, lavender is a beautiful and rewarding plant. It is one of the special plants, like roses, lilacs, and dahlias that many people name as their favorite. It has been cultivated and popular for thousands of years, and in the past two decades, as people have become aware of how easy it is to grow and noted its simple beauty, medicinal, psychological, and even spiritual herbal qualities, has become even more so. As I said in the new introduction, the demand for lavender is strong, and the future appears healthy, especially for those growers producing the highest quality plants.

Once, primarily a European export, lavender is now grown commercially all over the world. Barely a week goes by that we are not approached by growers from places as far-flung as Singapore to Missoula, Turkey, Bulgaria, South Africa, Poland, Ukraine, Mexico, and Guatemala, all wanting to learn to grow lavender. I recently sent two books to England, which is ironic, since commercial lavender cultivation first thrived in the British Isles.

Lavender's popularity has a lot to with something most home gardeners know—lavender is an easy plant to grow. It requires minimal care, does well in many soils, needs little water and fertilizer, has few pests or predators, and demands little maintenance. However, if you are thinking of investing in a larger planting, you'll want to pay attention to ways to minimize any waste of money or precious time.

A few years ago, a lovely couple in their late fifties came to the farm. They both held office jobs and he planned to retire soon. His intention was to start a lavender farm as their retirement occupation and, while she stood warily off to the side, we discussed growing lavender. He was a very careful guy, had done good research about number of plants per acre, what variety, and the suitability of their location. All he needed was to flesh out a few of the details before getting started. We were excited for him, so we asked a few intimate questions such as "How do you plan to mulch?" He replied with surprise, "Mulch?" Sadly, the poor fellow responded the same way to questions about weeding, watering, harvesting, and fertilizing. We were not trying to burst his bubble, we were just being honest about things he wanted to know. It's possible that the bubble did burst when I asked him, "Who is going to do the work?" At this point, his wife, who had heretofore been silent, raised an eyebrow and said, "Yes, who is going to do the work?" This was not the first time we had asked someone that question only to provoke the same strange look it always evinces until we explain that our farm is the result of two people doing all the labor, planning, marketing, maintenance, and thinking. "If you enjoy the work," we told him, "it feels good. But, if you don't enjoy working with plants and land, you should reconsider because there's a lot of work." When he mentioned that he was considering hiring out the work, we suggested he think things through again. Finally I asked him, "Are you doing this for personal enjoyment or because you want to make money?" He wasn't quite ready to answer that question but at least now he was better prepared to move ahead. To his credit, he was doing what needed to be done by asking questions and visiting other growers. Smart.

Labor costs affect profit as much as anything. Lavender is like any other agricultural crop in that way. I know that some of you are not worried about this. Some of you are not in it for the money; for you, the growing and maintaining are rewards unto themselves. Others of you have been farming, running orchards, vineyards, or doing nursery work, and you know the score, so if you are seeking a profit, you'll need to sit down with a pencil, paper, and calculator and do the math. Start-up, labor, maintenance, machinery, marketing, shipping, manufacture of goods, are all part of the overhead. If you love it, you'll probably be successful. If you don't love it and you're looking for a way to become rich, I'd reconsider it.

As you make your own entrance into the world of lavender, remember—a little knowledge will go a long way. While this is by no means a definitive book on growing lavender, it does come with a large body of experience and a common-sense approach to things. Growing plants, like so many things in life, comes down to patience, knowledge, and care. Have faith that the things you need to know will come to you through your work. Best wishes to you.

ও

SECTION ONE
REALITY CHECK

You know the one about the farmer who won the lottery? When asked what he planned to do with all that money, he said, "I guess I'll just keep farming until the money's all gone."

This part of the book is just a small dose of reality about the schedule, skills, and tasks required to do what you're thinking about doing if you grow plants for a living.

SIT BACK AND RELAX?

A friend of mine grew up on a North Dakota farm near the Canadian border. His parents and three brothers farmed twelve hundred acres of wheat, corn, soy, sunflowers, and whatever else they needed to survive. One summer, his parents visited our place and his Dad, looking at our modest fifteen acres, said, "Wow, it looks like a lot of work." I couldn't believe my ears. I said, "You farm twelve-hundred acres and *this* looks like a lot of work?" He said, "Oh yeah! All I do all day is ride a tractor and turn it when I come to the end of a row, but this looks like a lot of work." Farmers and nurserymen see the work that goes into things. They don't have the same romantic sense of things that people who haven't worked land tend to have. They know the reality.

Nancy and I sit down every year to try to figure out exactly what we do. We identified all aspects of our farm that require significant amounts of time. Here's what it looks like.

H = high demand   M = medium demand   L = less demand, but significant

Marketing (M)
Bookkeeping (L)
Banking (L)
Maintaining our sales shop (M)
Delivery of plants (L)
Plant production, propagation, planting, and transplanting (H)

Plant maintenance (H)
Garden maintenance (H)
Plant organization (H)
Ordering supplies (L)
Web site (L)
Watering (H)
Fertilizing (M)
Correspondence (M)
Harvesting (M)
Sales (H)
Product assembly (L)
Equipment maintenance (H)
Public relations (L)
Consultation (M)

Do not be discouraged! I only want to draw attention to the most important factor for success—your desire—because there is never any time when there isn't something you could or should be doing. What are you after - a successful business, a way to fill your days, a beautiful landscape? Keep your eyes on the prize!

ANNUAL SCHEDULE AND TASKS:

January: Closed. Do as little as possible or travel with the vast lavender fortune.

February: Closed. Inventory supplies, think, plan, order, and organize existing stock. Check written materials, advertising, web site, and set the calendar for the season. Greenhouse preparation

March: Closed. Prepare advertising, start weeding and feeding gardens and container stock. Grounds maintenance. Propagation for stock and plug sales. Transplant stock.

April: The same as March only double the work as things start growing faster. Advertising.

May: Open the farm on weekends. Ship plugs and transplant plugs. Lawns and grounds prepared for public. Sales area and shop prepared for the public.

June: Open the farm five days/wk. Transplant and ship plugs. Mow, weed, water, and organize. Be obsessively neat and tidy. Sales 30-50 hours/week.

July: Water all container stock! Welcome the public. Sales 30-50 hrs/week. Maintenance. Some harvesting. Water non-lavender beds. Prepare Lavender Celebration the end of July!

August: Sales. Harvest, exhale, and inventory stock for next year. Step up plants into larger containers. Prune plants. Water! Dry and situate harvest. Close for two weeks vacation.

September: Re-open but cut back to weekends. Fall sales. Fall cuttings. Reorganize greenhouses and stock. Put things in order for the rainy season. Check equipment.

October: Close the farm. Situate dried lavender. Some craft work. Plug & plant maintenance.

November: Closed. Bake pumpkin pie. Make sachets and other crafts with the flowers

December: Closed. Some holiday sales at markets. Bookkeeping.

&

KEEPING A JOURNAL

We started keeping a farm journal a few years ago. We write observations about the weather, dates of plantings, propagation, transplanting, any casual observations about soil, mulch, insects, fertilizer results, watering, and anything that comes to our attention. It helps us remember things that we know we won't forget, but do, and more important, when we look back at it, it holds insights that we thought insignificant at the time but which now explain things. We're not completely faithful about making entries, but the more you note, the more you learn.

&

SECTION TWO
PREPARATION

LOCATING YOUR PLANTINGS: CLIMATE

The first thing you need to know is: Will lavender grow where you want to plant it? If you live where the winters are not too cold, where there is adequate sunshine, and where you have water available and your soil drains, the answer (with some reservations) is probably yes. We know people growing successfully in Michigan, Iowa, Ohio, Massachusetts, New Mexico, Texas, Washington, Oregon, New Jersey, and California. Our farm is located at the foothills of the Coast Range Mountains in Oregon, where we tend to have wet winters with moderate temperatures (30s and 40s F) and few long stretches of freezing weather. We do have hot and dry summers, often

with temperatures in the 90s (35+ C.) Our greatest challenge is the monsoon-like rains that are common to the Northwest in fall and winter. Lavender comes from the Mediterranean where it normally does not rain 50 to 100 days each year. Mediterranean conditions are mild to hot during the day, seldom freezing, and then moist air brings water to the plants at night. Over the years we've seen lavender thrive despite these conditions, and in less than perfect soil. But, because of the rains, we space our plants further apart so that they will have air passing between them when mature, and to make sure they have adequate drainage.

Heat is Good! Dry is Good! Tropical—Not So Good!
Bitter Winters Where the Ground Freezes Deep—Not So Good!

The most important thing to understand is that some lavender varieties grow well in colder climates and some do not. If frilly edged lavenders like dentata, stoechas varieties, and some patented varieties such as Goodwin Creek don't handle the minor freezes we have here, it can be safe to assume they will not handle the even harder freezes of regions like high-elevation Colorado or Montana. But this doesn't mean you can't give them a try. Just don't go whole hog with a big planting or investment until you have a feel for things. Lavender is a wonderfully hardy plant, but it won't grow (well) everywhere. We receive a lot of interest from people who want to grow in very cold climates. I hate to discourage them, but I do, especially when they ask if it's possible to protect the plants in the winter. Anything's possible, but it's better to be realistic about your chances for success.

Almost all varieties thrive in hot and dry. If you have hot and dry, you're set, as long as you provide adequate watering. In hot and damp areas, like South Florida or other more tropical places, lavender is prone to being eaten by insects or harmed by various molds, so it's best to stay away from it there. A few years ago we drove across the country and gave plants to folks along the way from Bend (high desert) to Boston. Most of those plants are surviving, although we did give some to a woman in South Dakota too with the warning that they were unlikely to survive their 60 below zero winters. They didn't. A few years later she visited us and told us she kept her plants in pots and brought them inside for the winter. If you live somewhere where the winters are bitterly cold, where the ground freezes for long periods, you should consider growing a different plant.

LOCATING YOUR PLANTINGS: EXPOSURE

Exposure is a fairly simple concept. Exposure means how much sun your plants receive each day. Lavender loves sunshine. The more light (southern exposure in this hemisphere), the better. Sunshine is the source of energy (food) for plants, and lavender will grow stronger and healthier when given lots of it. Our main beds have good southern exposures. From March to October they receive no less than eight hours of full sun each day. More would be even better, but we live tucked into a little valley where the morning and afternoon sun is cut off by trees and hills. Lavender will grow in shade, but it won't grow as fast, have the majesty and uniformity that make it so attractive, and will not produce the same abundant blooms. You can try growing it in less sunshine, but we don't recommend it. If you're thinking about growing lavender, take some time to look at it in other places. Notice how and where it grows. Your own observations will establish a good foundation for your later success.

LOCATING YOUR PLANTINGS: SOIL

The traditional soil guidelines for growing lavender are to plant it in **sweet soil** (pH greater than 7) that is well drained, porous, with little **organic matter**, and to the eye "poor." Think gravely, sandy, crumbly, scratchy, and you have the idea. Lavender does best in this type of soil. We are not blessed with such soil, but instead grow our lavender in what we affectionately call Hamm Road Adobe: a plastic clay common to western Oregon that oozes in the winter rains, parches into cracking blocks resembling North African deserts in the summer heat, and is largely unworkable for much of the year; yet our lavender thrives in it! Still, it is not ideal, especially when any transplanting is necessary, or when the ground is saturated with water for such long stretches of time that the plants are threatened with water stress.

The closer you are to the ideal soil conditions, the better off you'll be. Think of lavender as having needs similar to grapes; indeed, the two crops are often grown together. Before you plant, make sure to test your soil **pH** -

A figure expressing the acidity or alkalinity of a solution scale on which 7 is neutral, lower values are more acid, and higher values more alkaline. It's a simple step and will tell you what to do. Lavender prefers alkaline soil but it can be grown successfully in less than perfect conditions. Acidic soil can be amended gradually with various limes until it comes close to the alkaline conditions desired. Heavier soils can also be improved to become more friable (easier to work, looser) but, of course, the closer your soil is to these conditions from the start, the easier your job will be. Once you have planted a large area, there will be little you can do to change the overall soil conditions.

Regardless of your specific soil profile, it is essential that the soil have adequate drainage. Few things kill lavender, but standing water (sump or bog) will do the trick. If you have heavier soils that drain slowly, you may want to place your plants on gentle hillsides or slopes that encourage drainage. Flat ground with well draining soils is great as long as there is adequate water in the summer. To repeat: Lavender is extremely drought-tolerant, but *some* water is necessary. Forget about boggy areas: no wet sponges. Also, within larger beds there may be low spots or puddle areas. In these areas we mound the soil to supply the necessary drainage. Mound growing involves simply making a small raised hill within which you place the plant. The mound creates a slope for drainage as well as more airy conditions for the plants.

Changing the basic qualities of existing soil is a tricky and costly affair and is never as good as putting something in the right place from the beginning.

ABOUT SOILS

Because soil is such an important part of the health of your plants, it bears special consideration. The soil you have in the ground your the most precious commodity. Ask any farmer. Literally thousands of years of knowledge have been handed down about maintaining quality soil. If you have the right soil, you're fortunate, if you don't you're out of luck. You can alter the character of soil but this takes time and sustained effort. The best bet is to find the right soil in the first place. Big-time agriculture of the past century has somewhat shifted that truism by amending (fertilizing the dickens out of) nutrient-poor soils. That's why places like the Imperial Valley in Southern California can raise vast amounts of produce on desert sand—just add water, tons of chemicals, and voila! The same is true of most nurseries. They don't really use soil, they use mixes of available material such as wood, recycle, compost, wood chips, river loam, peat, perlite, mint

compost, agricultural waste, seafood or meat byproducts, etc. Until they come up with something that allows plants to grow. Then they add large amounts of fertilizer and sell you a force-fed plant that looks good to the eye. Some of those plants will do okay once you put them in the ground; others will not, because often these chemical wonders look great but have been grown too fast to have the vigor necessary to survive on their own. Such is life. I'm not trying to preach about the virtues and vices of modern agriculture, just trying to help you to grow lavender successfully and have your customers stay satisfied.

The point is you'll probably need to buy soil from a supplier if you plan on raising your stock in containers. When you do, you'll encounter a confounding range of "soils." Some will be called potting mix, some garden compost, some organic mix, some mega fertilized mix, some economy mix. What matters for lavender is that the mix drains well but holds enough water not to go bone-dry. Also, plants in containers need to be fed. That means fertilizer. (See fertilizer section.) A few years ago we lost a large amount of plants (Really!) to a poor soil mix. Since then, I no longer accepted any claims about commercial soils. Instead I asked our supplier to give me samples of their mixes for free in exchange for our running tests of our plants in their soils. I placed the soil in unmarked containers and transplanted similar plants into each. Week by week I noted the performance of the various plants; lo and behold, after three months it was pretty clear what worked and what didn't. The results were dramatic. Okay, a scientist raised me and I like to do these things, but it was helpful. You may not want to go this far, but before you entrust what may be thousands of dollars of investment, you better know your soil is reliable.

Soil is so important that two to three times a year most nursery trade commercial publications we read talk about them. Soil is everything. The good news is you will find what works for you. There are many tried and true mixes or techniques, but remember, they're only as good as the last batch of materials that went into them. Develop a friendly and constructive relationship with your soil supplier and by all means deal only with people who are reputable and know what they're doing. Your destinies are linked. When it comes to soil, two familiar slogans come to mind: "The price of freedom is eternal vigilance" and "Trust but verify."

CB

CULTIVATION METHODS:

At the Sawmill Ballroom, we planted our lavender to fit the landscape of rolling hills. Our plants resembled contour lines on a map. We try not to intersect flowing lines with harsh planting angles. How you plant depends on your ground and the look you want. If you're growing for a production harvest, you may end up with plantings that are farm-like in rows, like corn. If you plan on having events and visitors, and showcasing a beautiful garden and serene setting, you may design a more garden-like aesthetic to your plantings. There's no right way, except to plant in ways that allow you to do what you want with your plants. It is useful to have a reasonably accurate measure of the square footage of your plantings in order to plan how many plants you need. Here are a few useful calculations.

A 100'x100' square planted on 3' centers, 3' rows will hold about 1056 plants.

A 100'x100' square planted on 3' centers, 4' rows will hold about 894 plants.

A 100'x100' square planted on 3' centers, 6' rows will hold about 578 plants.

****

An acre (100'x440') of plants on 3' centers, 3' rows will hold about 5000 plants.

An acre (100'x440') of plants on 3' centers, 4' rows will hold about 3740 plants.

An acre (100'x440') of plants on 3' centers, 6' rows will hold about 2500 plants.

SELECTING VARIETIES

Once you have selected your location, ascertained that the climate is good and that the soil and exposure are suitable, you're ready to select varieties. This is a fun place to be. There are varieties that have beautiful flowers, some that have sweeter fragrance, some that won't tolerate short winter freezes each winter, some that are easier to harvest; there are purples, pinks, white, yellow, red, and true lavender, small and large, plants that grow round and compact, others that sprawl. Some bloom in March, April, May, June, July, August, or September (where we are); some bloom every month of the year somewhere else.

It's time to ask yourself a few questions: what am I growing these for? For cut or harvested flowers, for fragrance, color, oil extraction, landscape value, foliage, time of bloom, to attract bees or tourists? Once you have answered that question, you have to ask, "Can I acquire the plants I need?" Even with the proliferation of lavender varieties and growers, it can still be a challenge to obtain the quantities and varieties you want.

LAVENDER VARIETIES

"A rose by any other name may smell just as sweet..."
It is not so with lavender.

In recent years there has been a proliferation of lavender names. Many of these "different" lavenders are simply trade names used by nurseries or retailers to distinguish their products, but there also are cultivars (variations on the same species) that distinguish the unique qualities of a plant. We grow nearly thirty varieties of lavender, and when we hear of a new variety we plant and grow it. This way we see for ourselves whether the plant is indeed unique or different. The most important information you will ever gather is what you can see with your own eyes and smell with your own nose. With the exception of oil content—what you see is what you get. Of course, it takes a couple of years to bring most lavender to full size and bloom, so you have either to be patient or spend a little time making sure of your supply. This means that name alone may not be a reliable way to select your plants. You'll need to familiarize yourself with the variety you choose based on experience, watching it grow, seeing it flower, and familiarizing yourself with its qualities. Cultivars do matter, because the same species can vary in size, bloom time, fragrance, and color. To put this simply, Abraham Lincoln and Mother Teresa were both the same species, but they looked a lot different. If you're buying plants from a nursery, make sure the plants come from their own stock or from a source you can verify. Many nurseries are simply retailers who buy their plants from larger wholesalers. There's nothing wrong with this, but your seller may not know your specific needs. Ask any supplier if the plants were propagated

in house. If the answer is yes, ask to see the mother stock and be sure it's what you want. If the answer is no, ask for the name of the supplier and give them a call. Reputable nurseries will welcome your questions. Another case of "Trust, but verify."

Don't worry, it's not as tough as it sounds. Growers all over the world ask this question and answer it. Usually they plant a *Lavandula angustofolia* for aroma, one of the purple varieties for color, and Spanish varieties for novel beauty and early bloom. We grow about 60 different varieties on our grounds, and we've looked at well over 100 different named lavenders. A few varieties have emerged as the best. This is not to say that each one isn't unique and worthy of consideration, but some of the differences are subtle, and really **it comes down to size, shape, color, time of bloom, foliage, fragrance, and hardiness.** In the back we list varieties by these characteristics as we've seen them here. Of course, some of these, in particular, time of blooming, will vary depending on your location. Again, I suggest you take the time to visit other growers. It's worth the effort.

C3

LITTLE DUCK

Little Duck came home to-
day, March 9th, almost a year to the day after she was born.

Little Duck was born on a Monday morning. We remember well,
because the day before Sunday morning that I walked out to the pond, a
pond filled with grasses along the edge, with rough skin newts popping to
the surface to grab some air from time to time, and masses and masses of
eggs from the hundreds of chorus frogs who fill the nights with their romantic croaking. It was early Sunday morning when I crossed the earthen
dam and was startled by the flush of baby mallards that emerged with their
mother. Nine in all, heading to the center of the pond where they were safe.
I was so excited I ran back to the house to tell Nancy, Ruby, and Dad, who
was visiting from New York. After all, it isn't every day that a family of mallards appears in your pond. It was a special event, and the rest of the day we
watched as mama duck led her charges around the tiny pond. Ruby, with
an eight-year-old's impatient curiosity, drew nearer and nearer to the duck-
lings, and actually came close, confirming that all young creatures share a
bond of trust and companionship. In the afternoon Mama Duck took to
the land, and by nightfall the ducks were gone, probably walking over the
hill to the more secure ponds below. We were sad to see them go.

The next morning we wandered the edge of the pond hoping to
repeat the previous day's excitement, but it was not to be. Mama Duck,
in her instinctive wisdom, had taken her family to a better place, less ex-
posed to the perils of an open pond with little hiding area, away from the
raccoons, the persistent hawks, cats, and coyotes. Some time passed and,
though we knew we would not see them again, we walked the pond again
the way we pursue a lingering vision or experience that we don't want to
fade, the way we smell a garment of a loved one, or stare at a photo. Then it
happened! Out of the weeds came a single little duckling. One. One duckling scurried across the pond barely able to stay upright, like the head of a
dandelion when it is blown across a short mowed grass. What was it doing
here, one duckling, where was its mother? Had this little bird stayed asleep
while Mama took its siblings to their safer place? Of course not. This little
duck was the late egg, the last egg to hatch; it probably didn't emerge until
the warmth of the next morning's sun gave it the spark necessary to peck
its way out. But what sort of world was it born into? Surely Mama Duck
would return to claim her child. Surely this new hatchling would not be an

orphan. And it was just that thought that tore at our hearts, especially my father, who could barely speak at the thought of this tiny little creature being left alone. What should we do? Should we capture the baby and raise it? Even if we wanted to, the duckling was too fast and wary of us to be caught. When we approached it, it simply shot out into the pond and paddled around out of reach. We marveled at how equipped the barely hours-old little creature was. When not harassed by our presence, it deftly patrolled the edge of the pond nipping at insects and weeds. It seemed to be eating, and then, later in the day, it nestled among some taller grasses and almost disappeared from view. It was so well concealed that, had we not known its resting place, we could not have seen it. We called it Little Duck, and decided that Nature would have to be the final say in its fate. That night we offered gentle prayers for Little Duck, thinking it unlikely we would see it in the morning.

The next morning, at first light, we rushed to the window and were thrilled to see Little Duck already actively making its rounds in the pond. It had survived the night. Could it continue? We were not optimistic, but hopeful, yes, for Little Duck had shown itself to be very capable. After a few days, we noticed Little Duck was growing. A miracle, this tiny orphan was feeding itself, hiding at night, napping in the sun during the day, and actually growing. A week into Little Duck's life, Dad said goodbye as he returned to New York, saying "Let me know about that duck, I sure hope it makes it." Off he flew, and every few days when we'd speak, he'd ask "How's that duck?" and we'd say, "So far so good, it's getting bigger." Soon, days became weeks, and Little Duck became familiar with us, enough so that we could walk near it in the pond, although when it left the pond it ran back if we came close. After all, it would be too much to expect any duck to abandon the safety of water. In a month Little Duck was not so little anymore, but took on the longer graceful form of a mallard. Each day was filled with concerns for Little Duck. Upon awaking, the first thing we'd check for was the presence of Little Duck. Coming home from work we'd ask each other, "Did you see Little Duck today?" "Was Little Duck out of the pond?" "Did Little Duck find a new place to sleep today?" Little Duck brought great joy to our lives, and I think reporting its survival to my father was the greatest joy. And then one morning, she was gone! Little Duck had shown us she could fly before she disappeared, and we thought she might leave, but from one day to the next the thought of her vanishing was terrible. Anything could have happened. There were countless raccoon prints in the mud beside the pond from their nightly patrols, and hawks would love duck for lunch. There were so many other animals that might come after this helpless bird, so when she disappeared, we grieved for Little Duck the way many people do when faced with the unexplained disappearance of a loved one.

Each day now we looked for Little Duck. We walked the other waterways nearby, hoping to see her, and frightened of what we might find we looked for signs of her demise. The tell-tale cluster of feathers that brings certainty to the fate of a vanished chicken, or the trail of delicate fur from a lost rabbit—these we were frightened to find, though we looked, hoping to bring closure to our loss. After a month we gave up. Little Duck was gone, and if there was any hope left, it was in the lore of animals that says they will return to their homes. That so many migratory animals seek the place of their birth to return to again and again.

Summer came and went and the pond went dry as it does every year. As I watched it recede, I thought ahead to March. In a climate so filled with winter rain that sanity was a challenge, I found myself looking ahead to the rains. It surprised me that something as simple as this orphan duck actually tethered me to the land in anticipation, that the life of Little Duck held my own life in suspense and bound my soul to this place. If people no longer held me the way they have in the past, Little Duck and freshly planted or pruned apple trees coming into their fruiting years held me now in the cycle of nature. My life had come down to the most simple of things, that I longed for Little Duck to return, for her survival against overwhelming odds, that we all shared the same hope for her, and that to be able to tell my father should this orphan whose birth and early days we all shared had come home, that in Little Duck was the sadness and the hope that we all carry, the losses, the loves, I prayed for the return of Little Duck.

Little Duck came home today, March 9th, almost a year to the day she was born. Looking out the window, I saw a sudden splash from the pond, a sure sign of disturbance of water, widening ripple, the delicate form of a slightly smaller female mallard, Little Duck, swimming in tandem with her a radiant green partner—Little Duck's companion. Nancy named her and her partner Anna and Joseph because today is the day Nancy's Grandmother Annie was born, later to marry Joseph. We all see what we long for in Little Duck. She is our miracle child.

I still call her Little Duck, however, our orphan survivor, returned one year later, grown and mature, to the pond of her birth!

3rd March 1998 © JEB

☙

SECTION THREE
LAVENDER CARE

OBTAINING STOCK FROM CUTTINGS, SEED, BROKERS, AND NURSERIES

Obtaining your plants is relatively simple. If you have tons of money and want to buy them, you probably can. Many varieties can be had as **plugs** (small starts not ready to go in the ground), as small 4-inch (these may be ready to be planted), or in gallon size (these should be ready to go in the ground). Plugs can be had for as little as 35 cents apiece, and come in sheets of 72-128. They need to be transplanted and cared for as long as it takes to mature them for outside planting. If you have an area to hold a few thousand transplants, and the time and inclination to do so, plugs are great. They can be obtained by speaking with a plant broker or reputable nursery that produces herbs and lavenders. Many nurseries will also contract to produce the plants you need. I cannot overemphasize the importance of dealing with a reputable nursery. Take the time to be clear about what you need and what they will provide. We've found the smaller mom-and-pop nurseries tend to provide higher-quality plants, although some larger nurseries do fine as well. The same nurseries that produce plugs for you will probably be happy to provide you with 4-inch or gallon plants, although, if you're buying a lot, most will need a decent lead time (6 months or more) and they will expect some form of advance payment. Buying 4-inch pots or gallons will be expensive ($1-10/plant), even in quantity, so you might want to consider something you will eventually do anyway—propagate your own.

PROPAGATION

Propagating plants is satisfying work. You also save money when you create your own plants instead of buying them. Seeing tidy little flats of cuttings lined up in the greenhouse (men love this) appeals to anyone with a sense of order and it is far and away the least expensive way to obtain stock. Propagating plants from known mother-stock allows you to produce exact replicas of the plants you like, both genetically and by appearance. You can also use a friend or eager volunteer to stick cuttings. People love to do this. We know a commercial grower whose elderly mother sits all day and sticks cuttings.

At the Sawmill Ballroom, our experience propagating lavender has evolved from "crude," hopeful cuttings to a somewhat systematic and very reliable technique, as well as schedules. Our first cuttings were the Tuscan cuttings mentioned in the introduction. Those cuttings were taken in Italy in January and stuck into the ground in Seattle in March; seven of the original twelve survived. They were simply stuck in the ground and they grew. Yes, you can do that!

From that "scientific" method, we progressed to placing numerous cuttings into boxes filled with 3/4 minus gravel. The idea for those boxes was "borrowed" from the movie *The Crying Game*, which has a scene where the main character is held hostage at a small farmhouse. The farm shed in the movie held what looked like nifty propagation boxes, so I just replicated them. It turned out that the design I copied was actually meant for holding seed potato cuttings to let them skin over before planting, but they worked great for us. The down side was that the roots could become entangled in the gravel, and teasing them apart could be fussy work. We used to stick about eighty cuttings in each of the boxes and produced all we needed. It wasn't until we decided to produce more plants, including enough to sell plugs that we had to change our method. What works for twelve doesn't always work for twelve thousand, or twenty thousand, or a twelve hundred thousand.

Since we made those first cuttings, we have propagated nearly seventy-five cultivars using various propagation mixes (potting soil, commercial propagation mixes, home-made mixes, straight peat, straight perlite, sand, and more), set cuttings with and without rooting hormone, employed bottom heat first with heating mats and now with heated benches, taken spring cuttings and fall cuttings, terminal cuttings, and side cuttings. What we have found is that things change from year to year and propagation is always an adventure. Fortunately, most varieties do well. Some cuttings root almost one hundred percent and thrive once rooted, while some are difficult to root and still others root and then fail to thrive. Propagation is a delightfully maddening blend of science, art, and care, and though we've got it somewhat "down," there are times when we wonder what the h— happened with those?

That said, here's how we do it.

You will need mother stock: larger plants that are healthy and strong. A small planting of mature plants can supply you with thousands of cuttings. How many you can take per plant varies between ten and hundreds. We often take cuttings off the container plants we're growing out in the nursery. The cutting actually stimulates the plants to a fuller and more pleasing look once they grow back.

TAKING CUTTINGS

When and how do you take cuttings? We find that our best cuttings come in the spring once the plants begin to "push." "Push" is just another word for starting to grow, showing new growth, showing a growth spurt. We like cuttings that come at the margin of the old and the new growth: not woody at the base, but not so new and flimsy that they have no stem structure. You do have to "stick" the cutting into the soil and you don't want it to crease or break. After you do this a while you begin to acquire a good feel for what a strong cutting looks like.

We have a saying at the SBLF: "Good cutting, good plant. Bad cutting, bad plant." We've learned this lesson too many times for it to be funny. Bad cuttings are not worth the effort. Even if they root, they will not thrive, and you will fight to keep them alive at all stages of their growth. Some people are great at taking cuttings. Nancy and Sasha, who used to work with us, are the best. Armed with a pair of spring-loaded snips and a basket, they head out and start snipping away. It takes a certain fastidiousness to sit and work your way around a mature plant and take precise well-matched cuttings, but it's worth it. Uneven cuttings pose later problems. Also, be careful not to over-cut on a plant. Take only what is good, and then stop. Many of us have a tendency to "keep going," and the cuttings become smaller and smaller and weaker and

weaker and before you know it you've broken the rule. Trust me on this. Really! **Good cutting, good plant. Bad cutting, bad plant.** Once the basket is full, cuttings need to be "stuck" right away. You don't want fresh cuttings to dry out or have any chance to deteriorate. While one person is snipping, another should be sticking them into moist soil or propagation medium. As mentioned previously, this can be many things. We use a commercial propagation mix, which is a lighter blend of peat, perlite, and sand. We saturate it with water until it has the consistency of brownie dough, and then we fill plug flats with it. AND START STICKING!

If you're going to use rooting hormone, this is the time. I wish I could offer a clear opinion on whether to use the hormone. Our experience tells us we don't need it, although we do occasionally use it on tougher varieties. You'll have to do your own trials on this and decide for yourself. Once they are ready to be stuck, whether dipped in hormone or not, we stick the fresh cutting snugly into the cell and cover one or two sets of nodes.

Once "stuck," the cuttings often wilt slightly in the first few days due to the loss of turgid pressure in them. A sure sign the cuttings are "taking" is when they return to a robust form as the pressure returns. We like to let our new flats of stuck cuttings rest out of sunshine and greenhouse or heating mats for a few days until they come back to form, but often we do not. As long as they are kept moist during this interval, they seem to do fine. They must not be allowed to "dry out" or the newly developing cells that will become roots will die and the cuttings will be lost. Do not plan any trips during the cutting stage until all your plugs are in pots or the ground!

STICKING CUTTINGS

Your friends can help you do this. Friends love to stick cuttings, but make sure you show them how before you turn them loose on one of the most critical tasks of propagation. You don't want fresh cuttings to dry out or have any chance to deteriorate. While one person is snipping, another should be sticking the cuttings into moist soil or propagation medium. We stick the fresh cutting snugly into the cell and cover one or two sets of nodes. A capable pair of hands can stick thousands of cuttings in an hour, but don't do this for too long or your back grows weary.

You also have an option of using rooting hormone when you stick the cuttings. Using rooting hormone adds a simple step to sticking a cutting when you "dip" or "roll" the soil end of the cutting into the rooting hormone, which is a talc-like powder. Some people swear by rooting hormone, but our experience without it, and then with a number of side-by-side trails with and without it, told us we didn't need it. Occasionally we use it on tougher varieties such as Munstead, which we are never very successful at rooting no matter what method we use. I suggest you do your own side-by-side trials with rooting hormone. Keep good records of how long the cuttings take to root, the rooting percentages, and how successful the transplants are, and then decide for your self.

GROWING CUTTINGS

Regardless of when you take your cuttings, they root better and faster when heated from below. We have a small greenhouse with heated benches covered with soil. The heated benches total 240 square feet—enough to accommodate about 130

propagation trays at one time. The heat comes from circulating hot water provided by an electric hot water heater and pumped by a small thermostatically controlled pump. The electricity to run this system costs about $100/month, and the benches cost about $2,000 to build. Our heated benches yield roots on most spring cuttings in about three weeks.

Temperature matters. We maintain the benches at about sixty degrees Fahrenheit. We keep thermometers in flats of cuttings to be able to read the temperature of the soil quickly. Don't trust automated watering or heaters in this stage, and don't turn these tasks over to a teenager who may be easily distracted by other things. At night the benches may become cooler due to changes in the outside temperature; you can regulate this with thermostats, although this involves using another piece of equipment that complicates your life and can fail. More important than maintaining a constant temperature is that the cuttings are constantly receiving the "bottom heat" that stimulates the rooting. You often read that 72 degrees Fahrenheit (22 C) is an optimal temperature for rooting cuttings. We keep ours cooler than that (60-68 F/14-20C) because the higher temperatures dry out the soil more quickly and place the young plants at risk of drying completely. Also, higher temperatures mean more watering cycles, which can leach fertility and change the pH of the soil. Watering tiny soil cells frequently stresses the rooted plants and results in higher losses. The tiny young roots of the new plants do not respond well to all of those changes—so we keep our benches cooler. There!

Contact, then non-contact. We like to have direct contact between the flat bottoms and the heated soil to maintain a moist and warm environment conducive to rooting. However, once the roots start to appear, we move the flats onto racks that are elevated about ¾ of an inch above the soil. The gap allows for air circulation and also maintains a physical barrier to keep the roots of the plugs from growing into the bench soil. If the roots grow "through" and into the benches, it's both a mess and a stress when you are ready to transplant or ship the plugs. The plugs love sending their roots into the bench soil, and you'll notice a marked vigor in them when they do— testimony to the fact that lavender plants thrive when they can expand their roots and regulate their water uptake. It just makes it harder for you to manipulate the plants

when you need to. I also rotate the flats to avoid this, gently turning the flats to break any tiny roots that haven't started to run down to the soil on the benches.

Size matters. Most propagation flats (also called seedling trays or cell trays) have round or square holes. I prefer the squares for no special reason. They are normally 11x22 inches in dimension and hold 50-225 cells per tray. Obviously, the more cells per tray, the smaller each cell. I prefer 72- and 128-cell flats because they hold enough soil to form a strong transplantable root mass. That transplantable root mass is called a plug. A plug is, simply put, a baby plant.

Larger cells like 72s and 50s are a little slower to root because the soil stays a little cooler, but they drain well, have room for extensive root formation, and can support a plug longer without stressing it. Fifty-cell trays make a great young plant that can be transplanted directly into the ground after being hardened off outside; however, they take more time and care to reach the desirable size. Our customers were often confused that we charged the same price for a flat of 50s as we did for a flat of 128s, until we explained that the former gave them something that would have almost no losses when transplanted and would save them labor and materials of another transplant step.

Cell size has an impact on the watering, drying, heating, and growth of the young plants. The more cells per flat, the greater the surface area. This results in quicker drying out of the flats on a bench. This is a significant consideration. It is easy to root cuttings: it is not as easy to make sure they stay healthy and thrive once rooted.

EARLY CARE

Once the cell flats are full of cuttings, we water them fully and gently with a watering wand and set them in the shade or on the heated benches. We prefer to let our new flats of stuck cuttings "rest" away from sunshine and greenhouse benches for a few days until they come back to form, but this isn't essential. As long as they are kept moist during this period, they do fine, but you don't want to stress new cuttings by placing them in a blazing hot greenhouse right away. Also, if your greenhouse is going to be bombarded with sun and high heat at this stage, shade cloth is a good option to curb the heat.

Once "stuck," the cuttings often wilt slightly in the first few days due to the loss of turgid pressure (that's a fancy way of saying they stop moving water through their vascular system after being "wounded"). It takes a few days for the stuck end to start drawing up water again, but a sure sign the cuttings are "taking" is when they return to a robust form as the turgid pressure returns. The cuttings will begin to stand up and boast of their recovery. One last reminder that **they cannot be allowed to dry out completely or the newly developing cuttings and then roots will die. Do not plan any trips during the cutting stage until all your plugs are in pots or the ground!**

Finally, another method we've used, and one that I like (even if I don't always use it), is to take the fresh cuttings and submerge them briefly in a "kelp" solution. "Algamin" is one common trade name for a pulverized kelp powder that forms a gelatinous solution when mixed with water. The gelatinous film coats the cutting and stops it from drying out. Kelp is also known to have root-stimulating properties, and I believe it, but I think the main value of this "dipping" is to "salve" the snip wound of the cutting and protect it from infection in the early stages in the soil.

FLOWERING CUTTINGS AND LEAFY CUTTINGS

Flowering cuttings: The terminal stems of spring cuttings often hold the flowering part of the plant. When these cuttings root and then grow, they send forth an energy-consuming flower. This can rob the cutting of a lot of its vigor and may lead to cutting failures. Rather than offer a rule about how to handle this, I can tell you that sometimes we trim the flower off and sometimes we don't. It all depends on the look and feel of things. Some cuttings have lots of base leaves and thrive when you take the flower off, while others wilt or become infected.

Another approach to this is to take only non-flowering cuttings. You can take side stems and even snip multiple cuts from them which root, although I don't like to wound the cutting too many times before placing it into a moist, pathogen-rich environment.

Leafy cuttings: A cutting with too much leaf may thrive for a while but can have problems when the leaves transpire (water exchange through leaf openings called stomata). Until it has a developed an adequate root complex to take up water, an overly leafy cutting may stress itself dry. We try to avoid heavily leafed cuttings, sometimes peeling away the lower leaves to expose nodes as well. Also, by avoiding heavily leafed cuttings, less waste accumulates as the older leaves die and fall onto the plug flat. Leaves will die off during the plug grow-out, so don't be too alarmed as long as the overall vigor of the cuttings is good. The converse of this is a cutting without enough leaf to gather sufficient sunlight. You can control some of this by providing adequate shade or sunlight.

We've often thought an ideal propagating and growing space for plugs would be a greenhouse with adequate shade cloth and rollup sides. This would have enough but not too much sunlight, while the air temperature would remain fairly cool except at the heated interface of root and bench. By being open on the sides, a healthy air exchange lessened the incidence of pathogens that thrive in stagnant, moist, greenhouse environments.

We have taken cuttings in the summer and often take some after pruning our plants after the bloom and allowing them enough time to heal and renew themselves with new growth. Those August, or even September, cuttings do quite well, although it has been our experience that they need more time to root, and once rooted, they are confronted with short days and declining sunlight and so are really going "dormant." When we time this properly, we achieve some of our strongest cuttings and plugs. They root, grow a little, and then slow down for the winter, which they spend in the greenhouse. Some varieties can withstand freezes, others do not, and so another consideration is your ability to keep stock from freezing. Fall cuttings have some virtues. By the end of February or early March, the wintered-over cuttings are hardened off, strong, vigorous, and do great when transplanted.

Once showing first root, cuttings normally take between three and six weeks to become "ready." We judge a plug ready to transplant once the root mass is intact enough for the plug to slip out of its cell with a gentle tug and hold together. A rooted cutting can be planted sooner if you are very careful and tender when transplanting it, although I don't recommend it. After all, the baby plug is young but once: let it enjoy its childhood.

Once the cuttings have all rooted, they no longer need the heated bench, and, when we can, we remove them from the benches and "grow them out" on the ground. Fully rooted plugs do best when transplanted into larger containers. If they sit in cell flats for too long they begin to stress. They will show a marked decline in vigor unless fertilized, indicated by loss of greenness or yellowing (also a sign of over-watering). The plug flats, if fertilized improperly, can have other problems. Topical application of fertilizers to plug trays can promote a thin film of algae that forms an air barrier. That alga scum can actually choke off the plug and kill it. To avoid this, we started dipping plug flats into fertilizer so that they receive the fertility at the root zone only. We simply mix fertilizer in a tray with water and set the plug flat inside it; this way only the root holes are submerged. The wicking action pulls the solution up, avoiding the algae mess. You can maintain plugs in flats, but the best thing to do with a fully ready, rooted cutting is to remove it from the cell flat and growing in a bigger pot or in the ground.

Before we leave this section, I want to address the common question we are asked about placing cuttings directly into the ground. I have to reiterate some basics here. A plug is just a baby plant. The smaller the plug, the less root and foliage it has. The smaller the plug, the more care it needs to ensure its survival. It cannot dry out, nor can it be over-watered. It cannot be trampled, nor can it be infested with weeds. It cannot be peed on by dogs or dislodged by the wind. The bigger the plug or plant, the more likely it is to survive when planted. We like to transplant plugs into 4-inch pots and grow them out for a while before transplanting into the ground, but if you plan on going directly from plug to ground, I suggest using 72s or 50s, because they allow extra root and more resilience in the plug itself. And yes, you can sow 128s, or even smaller, directly as long as you watch them carefully. You have to expect some losses but you can control some of this with adequate care, especially in the first month when the plugs are placed in the ground. We advise people that they will have to water their new plants for at least one full season, but lavender that is treated well and has a good start on life will soon root itself into the soil and require very little watering. Of course, this depends on whether you plant before the heat of the summer or afterwards.

It generally takes us six to eight months to produce a good-quality one-gallon plant that we feel good about selling or putting in the ground. The process can be speeded up with chemical fertilizers but we have found this produces weaker plants that look great but have much higher mortality when actually planted. We're not trying to beat an "organic" drum here, simply stating the results of our own experiences.

One last word on propagation: We have read countless books and magazine articles on propagation over the years, all with strong opinions about when to take the cuts, how to provide the heat, and what soil mixes to use. When all is said and done, it always comes down to taking the cuttings at the right time and then taking good care of them. You will find what works best for you by staying open to the workability of different approaches: Experiment and good luck.

Seed

Yes, you can grow lavender from seed. It is time-consuming, as is propagation via cuttings, but the uncertainties of pollination make it impossible to be sure of a plant that is genetically true.

We had a very hush-hush request from a business agent in New York who was trying to obtain lavender seed for a client in Poland. The "secretive agent," who knew little about lavender or plants, for that matter, wanted pure seed in a quantity that I loosely calculated could have amounted to every lavender seed produced in the entire world for the year. Maybe he knows something we don't.

Preparing the Ground

When we've done our larger plantings, we've prepared the area in a couple of different ways. Basically, because our soil is fairly heavy, we've loosened it with a rototiller while simultaneously "amending" (fertilizing) the area with lime or other soil conditioners. I love to rototill, but I am also aware that you can overdo this and hurt your soil. Think of this step as gently lightening and mixing your soil to make it only as loose as it needs to be for planting. If you're lucky enough to have good soil, this process will be much easier.

SPACING: HOW MUCH LAND DO YOU HAVE?

How you space your plants is one of the most significant decisions you make. (See the Cultivation Methods section for density calculations.) How you weed, harvest, and maintain your plants may be determined by your spacing. Wider row spacing allows for easier access for wheeled vehicles such as tractors, mowers, wheelbarrows, carts, or even ATVs, which many growers now use. Wider spacing makes pruning and harvesting easier, but it also means less area is planted and leaves more room for weeds to grow. Narrower row space means more plants per area planted and fewer weeds, due to the plants forming a canopy that keeps weed growth down, but it also means less access for the vehicles or tasks mentioned above. It's always a tradeoff. There are also aesthetic considerations; for example, do you want long snaking rows of plants forming contiguous lines? Or do you want individual plants that have individual character?

How you space your plants depends on the size of the plant at maturity and on the look or harvesting technique you plan to use. At the Sawmill Ballroom, we tend to space our larger plants (plants that grow to a diameter of 3 feet, such as Tuscan and Provence, among others) on 3-foot centers with 4-foot rows. That way we can always walk between the rows once the plants are mature, and the plants gently "kiss" their edges for what we find a pleasing look. We tend to space smaller cultivars (e.g., Hidcote, Munstead, and others) on 2- to 3-foot centers and rows of 3 feet. The largest plant we have reaches a diameter of about 3½ feet, so we plant these 4 feet apart in rows 5 feet apart. And, because we live in a wet climate, we leave the extra space for airflow in the wet seasons. There is no hard and fast rule. Like a lot of things, it's a "feel" thing, and the more you grow the more you'll trust your own feelings.

Hopefully you've done a few test plots and know the size of your plants, so you can make a smart decision on spacing. In Provence, France, where they use machine harvesters, the lavender fields are often planted in long rows about 6 to 8 feet apart. Because we harvest by hand, we lay our plants out to form rows with walking space between them. We also like to have the rows flow with the natural contours of the land. We do this by laying strings or ropes so we can see what the lines will look like. Then we simply move along with a spacer stick, planting along the rows. Some people use a grid system, which works fine as well. You can plant lavender more densely so that the mature plants form a drift or "solid" area, but they will be hard to access for chores like fertilizing, pruning, weeding, or cutting flowers. Think ahead about what you anticipate doing with the plants, then proceed with your design. There are some remarkably creative design ideas. I'm sure yours will be one. Have fun with your ideas.

PLANTING

If you've done your preparation, you are now ready to plant in a large and inviting open space, fully mulched, and begging for plants. Your ground is like a stretched and primed canvas waiting for color. Planting any plant is like moving to a new home—it takes a little while to settle in.

When to plant depends on where you live. We try to plant in the early spring (March), or the early fall (September). Here's why. If we plant in early spring, the plants have a chance to establish themselves with good roots before the very hot weather sets in. This means less stress on them, and for us when it comes to watering. An established lavender plant requires very little water. By planting in the fall, we skip the heat of the summer and start the plants when there is still some warm weather for them to grow and establish roots before going dormant. Fall plants become well established and are vigorous the following spring. We have planted in the summer; those plants did great, but we had to water them at least every other day for almost six weeks!

There are no particular requirements for planting lavender beyond preparing a hole deep and wide enough to set the plant into the ground easily where it will then be covered to the base of its stem/trunk (where the root mass meets the stalk). If you haven't fertilized the entire area to be planted, you may wish to add a small amount of organic fertilizer and "scratch it" into the loose soil in the hole. If the root mass in the pot is congested and tight, you can gently twist it to break it apart some, but don't start tearing it apart: be firm but loving. Then gently back-fill around the root mass as if you are tucking the plant in. Not so tight and tamped down that you compact the roots, and not so loose that you leave the plant in a hole with air pockets all around it. It's another feeling thing and you will come to know it pretty quickly.

Worthy of mention is how new plants are subject to "wicking" away of water when they are first planted. If a wet root mass is placed in a dry soil hole, the dry soil will draw the water from the root mass. This can kill a young plant. That's why it is important when transplanting to keep the surrounding soil moist. This goes double for plugs or smaller plants that can be wicked dry very quickly on a hot day. If you're transplanting a lot of plants in hot conditions, you need to pre-water the ground or the holes so you don't jeopardize the young plants. You may want to lay a drip line over the area to be planted well in advance of transplant time. This is a small step but it is a vital one.

MULCHING

Weed suppression is essential for the survival and presentation of your plants. For most lavender plantings, the most difficult time for weeding will be in the first year when the plants are small and there is lots of open ground around them. Once they mature, they will actually suppress weeds on their own by forming a beautiful canopy of foliage that is the familiar beauty of well-tended lavender fields. Few challenges inspire more innovation and bad judgment than how to weed; for thousands of years gardeners and farmers have been coming up with methods to lessen the task of weeding. A few of these methods even work; most do not. True, there are some beautiful and well-designed raised plantings that cover each lengthy mound with landscape fabric and run irrigation down them. This works as long as you keep the weeds down in the paths and never let any weeds encroach on the fabric itself. Should that happen, you end up with a lot of weeds and weed roots woven into your fabric in a mess that will have you pulling out your hair. You can also space your rows wide enough apart that you can run a riding mower or small tractor down the middle often enough to keep the weeds at bay. Sooner or later, though, for a host of reasons, you will become familiar with the world of mulching. Mulch is any material you place on top of growing grounds in a thick enough covering to suppress the growth of weeds. Rocks, pebbles, wood chips, composts, aged manures, beauty bark, leaves, grass, and straw are all common mulches; we've used most of them, often taking what was available to us at a reasonable cost.

When the tree pruners in our neighborhood needed to dump fine hardwood chips, we used chips, even though most wood chips rob nitrogen (we figured buying nitrogen was easier and cheaper than buying high-quality mulch). When the power company clears the electrical lines and has trucks of free chips, needles, and leaves, we take them, and when we feel flush and want to plant a new bed we even buy a commercial mulch, of which there are many in the land of forest byproducts. If we have to pay for it, Nancy prefers mulch that enhances the soil and is loose enough that we can pull newly opportunistic weeds with little effort. We've used mixes of steer manure and mint compost, which add nitrogen and meet the rest of our criteria. Whatever the product, we apply a generous layer (3-4") of mulch on a new bed before planting, then plant into it. There is no "right" way to mulch, there's just what works for you and what's available and suitable where you are.

Mulch is essential for us because we do not use chemical weed killers. Nancy can weed faster than anyone I know, but weeding a large area is still time-consuming and difficult work. A thick pre-mulching gives your plants a head start on weeds long enough to grow big enough to crowd out or canopy weeds. The weeds, however, will always find a way in, so you need to understand that mulching is part of the game. You may wish to become familiar with some of the newspaper and cardboard mulch techniques (covering sod or weedy areas with paper before applying the mulch material). If you're still confused about mulch, try this: take a piece of cardboard about 4'4' and set it flat on the ground in your garden. Mark off another space the same size right next to it. Then do nothing. At the end of a hot day, feel the area without the cardboard, then lift the cardboard and feel it. I think you'll understand mulch better now.

WEEDING

Whether you have a small planting or a large one, keeping your plants weeded is important for their healthy growth. The need to weed is simple—weeds compete with the lavender for water, sunshine, soil nutrients, and space. And weeds love these nicely prepared beds ready with space and nutrition. As I've already mentioned, Nancy can weed faster than anyone I've ever seen. She moves through a bed like a vacuum cleaner, picking out the pesky dandelions, chickweed, thistles, and other unwanted visitors by their roots. But even she cannot keep up with the weeds in the larger beds. Therefore, we employ techniques and materials that minimize the invasion of weeds, and then make it easier for us to remove the ones that do come more easily. In our first major planting, where we converted a large grass area into a planting bed, we mulched with coarse wood chips over a thick (six-sheet) layer of newsprint. This "newspaper" mulch has been in favor for some time, and is especially welcome now that most newspapers are printed with nontoxic soy-based inks. The paper and mulch layer forms a barrier to the existing grass, quickly killing it, while the chips keep out other weeds. Eventually, worms eat the newspaper and the chips decompose into soil. Even though plain wood chips actually take nutrition out of the soil to decompose, over time we think it's worth it. In our second large planting, we rototilled the sod, thus eliminating the need for the paper layer.

This area was then mulched with a blown mix obtained from our local forest products supplier to 3-4" deep. Most areas now have some form of these mulches made from recycled wood, yard waste, and other ingredients. You'll have to do some checking to see what's available in your area. After we applied the mulch (actually coming up a little short—check your math carefully or ask the supplier to figure it for you), we planted into the bed. Pulling any weeds that come into this bed is much easier than pulling from our other beds. I'm going to stand on a soapbox here for just a second. I have to be honest about weeding: It is the one challenge that has ever tempted us to resort to chemicals. There are times when the weeds overwhelm you and the thought of spraying something is appealing; but then we remember why we started doing this in the first place—to bring beauty to the earth, not to use harmful "shortcuts" for killing weeds. Besides, weed-killers are actually very expensive, they may leach into the waterways around us, and despite manufacturers' claims about how harmless they are, we simply do not believe it. In the end we always do our weeding the old-fashioned way, by hand, with a load of chips or mulch, and start hauling with a wheelbarrow. In the long run, it is probably cheaper to do it this way (even if you have to hire someone for a day) and it's a way to work with nature instead of in opposition. Regardless of what weeding methods you choose, remember that it is part of what you do, not something that is in the way of what you do.

Fertilizing

Fertilizing your plants is generally pretty simple. If your beds are well prepared ahead of time, you won't need a lot of fertilizer. We dress our plants annually with a slow-release balanced (equal parts nitrogen, phosphorous, and potassium) organic fertilizer; every other year we lime our beds to maintain the sweet conditions lavender prefers. Where we live, our soils are naturally more acidic, so we lime, but friends of ours across the mountains and in other parts of the country and world where soils are naturally basic don't have this need.

We recently added a basic soil-conditioning mix to our older beds, mainly because the plants have been there for some time and seemed to need a little boost. I've also started to foliar spray all the plants from time to time (every two to three weeks) with a 12/8/2 organic seabird guano mix. The stuff stinks like crazy, though for me it evokes fond memories of when I worked on a Russian factory fish processing ship! Nobody else here likes to use this mixture, but as common wisdom might lead you to believe, it smells so bad it must be good. (I also like to use the sprayer.) Another reason we use it is that we noticed our potted nursery stock grew slowly in the commercial soil mix. Rather than using poor soil and heavy chemical fertilizers, we opted for good soil with healthy organic fertilizers. Growing in containers has different requirements than growing in the ground, especially in a wet climate where nutrition washes out of pots quickly. Fertilizing can be a low-yield/high-cost game unless you know what you're after and have the experience to achieve it. I suggest you read farm supply catalogs for everything you can find about fertility. Remember, as you work with your plants you develop an awareness and intuition about them. You see them grow and you can tell what they need. Keep watching and reading and you'll know what to do to keep them healthy. Our basic philosophy is the less intervention the better.

CARE

Of all the things you do, taking good care of your plants is the most important. Care means being with them often enough to see their changes. We like to "walk" our plants a lot, sometimes multiple times in a day. Care is paying attention to the weather and other aspects of your environment. Care is noticing what insects and birds are involved with your plants; it is watering, feeding, and checking the soil around a sick plant. Care is taking time to have the people who help you understand why you do what you do. Care is trusting your intuition and knowing that most shortcuts don't work, don't save you time or money, and that there are no substitutes for doing things the right way. Care is choosing your plants wisely. Care will make you the expert.

WATERING

When planted in the ground, lavender is an extremely drought-tolerant plant. In the Mediterranean it sits on sparse soil hillsides that are baked in the dry summers by 100-degree days. The rest of the year it receives intermittent rainfall. However, the porous soil allows it to grab water through condensation in the cool and moist evenings. If you have these conditions, you will probably never have to water your lavender for its basic survival, though watering may still be desirable to produce robust and juicy-looking plants. If you can't water, you'll have to be a little more observant and thoughtful. Making sure your plants are "established" is the key. This means having their roots well developed into the soil. Lavender will usually send its roots deep and wide enough to meet its water needs. Since I covered this in the planting section above, I won't repeat myself here. We live in a wet climate. If anything, our concern is too much water. Our soils are heavy clay that retains moisture even when the summer temperatures reach above 100 degrees. So, once our plants' roots are established, watering is not necessary. You will need to know your soil, watch your plants, and take your cues from them. If you have coarse, rapidly draining soil that dries quickly, you may need to water, especially if your nights are low humidity. In any case, you probably will not need an elaborate watering system unless you have an extremely large planting where you cannot reach plants with sprinklers or a hose. If you receive even modest amounts of rain you probably won't need to water. On the other hand, if you live somewhere like Tucson, Arizona, you'll probably have to water, but if you mulch you won't need to water as much.

Whatever watering system you devise, try to make it simple and reliable. I never like to place my entire livelihood in the hands of a cheap switch or automatic system that can fail. Nancy and I wake up every morning, we know the weather, we walk the plants, and we evaluate what they need. After four weeks of 100-degree weather, we dig into the soil and assess the moisture, and we look at the plants.

Further, even though it is a drought-tolerant plant, lavender enjoys and thrives when it receives water; the flowering is more abundant, although the oil content is somewhat less intense, and the foliage has a fuller, more vigorous look. As with many things, watering versus not watering depends on your conditions and your purpose in growing. One last thing: Lavender loves maritime conditions where fog and cooler evening air bring it all the water it needs. I am always amazed to see how abundantly full of flowers lavenders are when living in maritime conditions.

HARVESTING

I've heard it said that some people are planters, some tenders, others harvesters. In the world of lavender you will become all of these. For preserving the lavender flowers, harvest when the flower heads of the lavender are just about to open, before they fully open their petals. This keeps the tiny flowers intact and they last longer. It also preserves the fragrance longer as the oils are more concentrated. Most varieties of lavender bloom over a long period of time. You can "pick" flowers over the entire bloom period and harvest all of them, although in larger plantings this is often impractical. We harvest our plants at the peak of the bloom—when most of the plants have the fullest amount of choice flowers. We do so by hand, using a wonderful tool Nancy discovered years ago, a simple hand-held serrated Japanese scythe. We just move along, grabbing bundles of flowers and, with a swift and steady pull, sever the flower stalks cleanly. Because the stem lengths vary, we try to harvest as long a stem as possible; then, if when we need to, we cut them to a uniform length later. Once cut, you can use the bundles fresh. The bundles will be lovely for about a day unless you chill them in a cooler the way commercial flower growers do. Chilling

can extend the fresh condition of cut lavender and allow for shipping. A friend of ours who owns a flower shop knows a lot about this. If you need to know more on this, talk to your local florist or flower wholesaler. A fresh-cut lavender bundle is a rare and rich experience! Life is always good when the fragrance of lavender surrounds you. If you're growing in quantity, most likely you'll need to dry the flowers as described below in the section on drying flowers.

PRUNING

While pruning lavender is not essential, it is desirable. Proper and timely pruning stimulates new growth, controls size (to some extent), and renews the vigor and robustness of plants. We prune after harvesting the flowers in July (your timing may be different). Pruning in late July gives the plants time to put on new growth before entering winter dormancy. Nancy prunes with her hand pruning shears, but you can also use electric hedge pruners. Don't prune so much that you leave no green on the plants, these are the leaves the plant needs to harness the sun and grow strong. I think of it as going to the barber for a trim, rather than a shaved head. Spring pruning of older plants also produces a fresh and vigorous foliage but runs the risk of removing the flowering portion of the plant. That's why we prefer after-harvest pruning. A common question we're asked is about older plants becoming woody, irregularly shaped, and "gnarly." This usually happens with traditional English varieties like Munstead and, although you can prune these plants to shape them, it usually doesn't work very well and the results are slow. We encourage people to choose the shape of a plant they like and also to appreciate that even gnarly plants produce beautiful flowers. Also, avoid pruning when there is a risk of freezing before the plants heal from their pruning wounds (about two to three weeks). Freezes of newly pruned plants can cause death do to infection.

Worthy of note in this pruning section is a small account of a woman who bought ninety Tuscan lavender from us to plant her sloping city lot. Those plants filled her street-facing yard, and for years were the splendid envy of the neighborhood. She didn't prune her plants, and as they grew larger, the "arms" began to open and the plants lost their perfect round shape. Nine years into her plants, she asked us what to do to restore the look she desired. Normally, we would recommend removing and replacing the plants. Tough it's a little more costly, it's more reliable than gradual pruning to restore the shape of the plants. In this case, however, since it was mid-spring and there was nothing to lose by trying something different, I suggested she cut the plants back to their base, water them, and see if they come back. I know that growers in warmer climates (Melbourne, Australia) do this as part of their routine cultivation. If it didn't work, the plants would die, she could remove them and replace them, but if it did... And it did! In fewer than three weeks, aided by the warming days, the addition of water, a little fertilizer, and good fortune, all ninety plants began showing new growth. Before long she had a full and compact bed of thriving lavender again. By the end of that summer, the plants looked as good as before. There wasn't much flowering that year, but the next year was as good as ever.

PREDATION

To date, we have lost few plants to predation from insects or other animals. The Oregon Nursery Inspector who checks for various pests regularly inspects us. When he first drove into the driveway, we were nervous thinking, here's another thing we have to deal with, but it turned out he was very helpful, knowledgeable, and left us with a certified clean bill of health and stickers to prove it on shipments out of state. He sees all the nurseries and so was a wealth of information. There are root pests like naturally occurring Sympalans (garden centipede), which nibble at the roots of young transplants. We see them occasionally but have not found them to be a problem. We've also lost a few plants in the ground from moles digging tunnels around the roots. Interestingly, the plants probably died from the tunnel filling with water in the winter and drowning the roots. More pleasures of living in a wet climate! Of course, we have books about garden pests and are on the lookout for any hostiles that love to live with lavender. This is another thing to note in your journal—common or uncommon insects you may find with your plants and when. Over time, your notes may help you understand cycles and avoid problems. We also have two donkeys who, when allowed to roam freely, love to nibble the plants, although we think this is more to irritate us than because they like them. I do, however, worry about what would happen if our neighbors' Belgian horses were to escape from their pasture and head our way.

LOSSES AND DISEASES

We have been relatively disease-free at our farm. Occasionally we see some "wilting" of early flower stems. We've lost some older plants to a confirmed root rot and some plug transplants in pots to a soil-borne fungus in the greenhouse. Our loss of older plants came after an extraordinary year of rainfall (100+ inches), and, though the agent of death probably has a Latin name (phytothera), we suspect drowning. Most plants simply cannot survive having their roots in so much water. Lavender is not mangrove: it does not have gills. A fungus I read about in a plant pathology textbook most likely caused the wilt-off. We tend not to be terribly concerned about things like that. The wilting stopped on its own. We don't ignore it; it was duly entered in the journal, and we keep an eye out for anything that may be related to it (my daughter thinks it only happens on stems where spit bugs settle), but we're not going to start spraying a fungicide all over the place to save a hundred stems of flowers out of fifty thousand!

Our approach to plants is the same as our approach to our own bodies: the fewer drugs the better. We fixed the rot problem by removing the damaged plants, liming the area around them, and replacing them with new plants in raised mounds. We solved the fungal problem by keeping our greenhouse open on the sides to allow more air circulation, and by growing more plants outside. Greenhouses are mixed blessings. They keep us dry, but they also create artificially moist conditions for fungi. Most greenhouse growers use heaters and fans for air exchange and circulation to address these problems. We simply rolled up the sides and accomplished the same result.

Lavender is a hardy plant. Older accounts of the English lavender nurseries tell of losing whole plantings to something called "Shab." I suspect this is phytothera but have not been able to confirm my suspicion. I likewise suspect that there is a wide variety of things that will injure lavender in places that are generally ill suited for growing it. We are fortunate to have a plant pathology lab at Oregon State University; if we see something suspicious, we send them a tissue sample and they send back an exhaustive list of scientific words to describe their findings. So far so good.

As you develop your own plantings, especially if you propagate your own stock, you will periodically encounter unexpected losses of healthy plugs, nursery plants, or field plants. ***Plants die from time to time.*** Usually we have a feel for why—a late freeze after early Spring pruning, roots being disturbed by moles, plants sitting in a low spot after a winter with 100 inches of rain! If your losses are sporadic, you don't always need to know why, but anything beyond normal losses should be checked. Most states maintain a plant pathology lab through their agricultural university's *Extension Service*. There are also commercial labs all around the country that do soil testing, and books about plant pathology that may be useful.

GREENHOUSES

Greenhouses are wonderful things. We live in a climate where it rains about seven or eight months a year. Greenhouses are large spaces where the rain doesn't fall. They extend the growing season on both the early and late sides, they generate extra heat for hot-loving plants, they allow us to take earlier cuttings for propagation because the plants wake up and grow sooner. Keeping rain off contained plants saves soil, saves fertilizer, and maintains pH. We like greenhouses. However, they also can

be moist and tropical, and lots of fungi and bacteria thrive in these conditions. There are many greenhouse "growers" around who are constantly fighting fungal problems. They spend considerable money and time on antifungal sprays. We're not interested in doing this: we don't like the chemicals, and we don't think it's necessary for what we're doing. Greenhouses also have a damaging effect on soil. The daily cycling of hot and cold, the greater range of temperatures and its effect on drying and watering tend to wear soil out. The warmth of a greenhouse can also promote algal growth and form a choking skin on plug flats and container stock; this suffocates the soil. On balance, I think greenhouses are useful. Depending on your needs and location, they may be essential. With air circulation fans you can avoid many common problems, and you may want a heated greenhouse for some things. Summing it up: we keep plants in greenhouses to keep the rain off them and give them an early start on growth for cuttings. Once we take our cuttings and once they've rooted, or the larger plants we keep in greenhouses are looking good, we take them outside into the open air.

C3

DEER...

Most of the time deer do not eat lavender! There are a lot of beautiful deer here and they eat almost everything else, but we have not fenced our plantings or kept a dog to chase the deer away. Fields and forests surround  us and there are plenty of other things for deer to eat. At one time there was a deer path traversing one of our large beds, something we liked to show people when they doubted our claim about the deer not eating the plants. In the past few years we've found newborn deer sleeping between rows of potted plants that were hidden by their mother, while she went off to browse on plants other than lavender. Last year, while my father was mowing a tall grass area of the farm, he stumbled onto a sleeping baby deer. There are a lot of deer here. They raid the vegetable garden, they nibble young fruit trees, they walk into greenhouses and eat young roses if the door is left open, they eat fallen apples and love tulips, but they do not eat lavender! We know of only two exceptions worthy of note: One is Orcas Island, Washington, where island-confined deer expand their diets to include whatever is available and are known to munch on rusting automobiles; the other is a Jesuit sanctuary on the Oregon coast where the deer are so tame, they come in the kitchen to make their tea in the morning (one was found reading this book in front of the fire!). We have many plants growing successfully in the South hills of Eugene where deer pressure is notorious. So confident are we in this claim that we offer a guarantee on our plants in this region. I think you'll have the same good luck. You can have deer and a beautiful landscape. You can grow large fields of lavender without the costly investment in a secure deer fence. All those guarantees aside, it is always wise to do smaller sample plantings before going full tilt.

CB

Section Four
After the Harvest

Oils

There are a lot of things "You can do in the world . . . there are a lot of things you should do . . . and there are a lot of things maybe you shouldn't do." I am the son of a chemist but I don't distill oils for a living, although if I had fifty acres of lavender in a two-cuttings/year climate, I might.

Essential oils of lavender are extracted from lavender flowers, leaves, and stems by a process of steam distillation. Steam distillation involves injecting steam into a vat of lavender material. The super-hot steam breaks down the vegetative material, releasing the oils from the plant. The hot-oil-carrying water is circulated and cooled and the oil (which is lighter than water) is then decanted. Commercial oil producers use a wide variety of steam distillers. Many are custom-made, but you can purchase small- and large-scale distillation equipment from a variety of sources, and there is no "one size fits all" recommendation for which ones to use.

Steam distillation is commonly employed to obtain the oils of various herbs. It is important to understand that it takes a lot of bulk to extract a little oil. With a good yielding oil plant, you can expect about a 2% yield of oil from your plants. That means you'll yield about 2 pounds of oil for every 100 pounds of flowers you start with. How much bulk you harvest per plant can vary widely by variety and by year. At the Sawmill Ballroom we didn't distill oil, but we did occasionally weigh samples of the plant harvest to have an idea of the yield in case we ever decided we did want to make oil. On a mature bed of lavender, our yields per plant (hand-cut and well-tended) for Provence lavender (a less desirable oil-producing L. *intermedia*) was about 1.5 lbs per plant. Our most fragrant plant, Tuscan (a desirable L. *angustofolia*), yielded less than half that amount.

One gallon of oil weighs about 7 pounds and you can realistically expect a yield between 4-15 gallons per acre. You can produce more flowers by fertilizing and watering, but that may result in lower quality oil. The Tuscan lavender that was un-watered and small-yield had the most aromatic and highest quality oil.

A typical row-cropped lavender planting would accommodate from 2000 to 4000 plants per acre. That translates to 3000-6000 pounds of harvest per acre for Provence and 1500-3000 pounds for Tuscan. At a high extraction figure of 2%, the Provence might yield 60-120 pounds (8-17 gallons) of oil and the Tuscan 30-60 pounds (4-8½ gallons). These figures are higher than any I have ever heard or read from any commercial grower.

In February 2008, I found lavender oil prices ranging from 400 to 1500 dollars per gallon. Organic, L. angustifolia oils were the highest priced There are growers who make money on oil, but I want to make it very clear here that, if you intend to go into oil extraction, you'd better learn everything possible about marketing, distillation, and growing. It takes labor to grow, harvest, extract, bottle, and sell the oil, and it bears close consideration in terms of profitability as a bulk commodity. If you can "add value" to it by selling high-quality oils at a premium price in small quantities direct to the public, you may be able to make a go of it.

Both lavender oil and lavender-oil economics are highly volatile, so use caution in either endeavor.

FRESH CUT AND DRIED FLOWERS, FARMERS' MARKETS AND FLORISTS

Summer in Lorane is reliability hot. While some lavender varieties begin blooming as early as May, the overwhelming bulk of our bloom comes in July and August, when we cut, hang, dry, and then sieve our flowers over a period of about two to four weeks. We bind the freshly cut bundles with rubber bands and hang them upside down in a dark, dry place for two to three days, or until the flowers begin to fall away from the bundles when gently disturbed. The size and stem count of the bundles vary

depending on variety, but for all varieties it is important that they not be so thick as to prevent the flowers from drying.

In Lorane, even summer evenings can be moist and if the cycle of daytime heat and evening humidity goes on too long, the flowers can deteriorate. Many smaller bundles are preferable to fewer large ones. We like to dry and sieve the flowers before any molds or dust can contaminate the sweet fresh smell of the flowers. Once the bundles are dry, the flowers fall off easily as we roll the bundles over a ¼" mesh hardware cloth screen into plastic tubs. Keeping the flowers dry is important for preventing dust, molds, and mildews, all of which will ruin the sweet smell of the precious flowers. Some people claim to be allergic to lavender, and certainly some are, but we suspect most have allergies to the dusts and molds. Once they have been sieved, we seal the flowers in airtight zipper-locked bags. I have considered using a vacuum sealer to preserve the freshness of the flowers but worry about compressing the flowers too much. Zip-locks have worked well for us. Once the flowers are bagged, we place the bags in rigid plastic containers that we store in a dark and dry place. If you wish to preserve the dried bundles of harvested lavender, you will also need a dry and dark storage area. Our drying sheds started as a dark bedroom, expanded to a shaded 10'20' woodshed, and later to the inside of a renovated barn that is weatherized and dry. Darkness prevents the color from being bleached out of the flowers and preserves the fragrance.

This is important. Why go through all the trouble of harvesting, drying, and storing your beautiful flowers, and then let them deteriorate in an unsuitable storage place? Of course, you may have very little left once people start calling to buy flowers for soaps, sachets, gifts, or teas.

Well-preserved lavender retains its color and fragrance for years, but, as with any herb or spice, the freshest harvest is always the best.

LAVENDER IN THE KITCHEN

If you "Google" lavender recipes, you'll discover an expanding world of lavender cookery. It is used in herb-tea blends, cake, biscotti, bread, and pastry flavoring, in ice cream, with champagne, or in savory meat dishes such as lamb. As a grower, if you plan to sell lavender for cooking, it is essential to produce lavender of only the best quality, from a chemically free source; it should be something you would eat yourself. Many restaurants and food manufacturers need lavender: you can supply them. Some growers claim to have lavender honey as well. We keep bees and find an abundance of both honeybees and bumblebees on the flowers; it appears to us, however, that the lavender is primarily a source of pollen, not nectar for honey.

MEDICINAL AND COSMETIC USES

In the past ten years lavender has surged into the health, cosmetic, and medicinal markets. Lavender is used for aromatherapy, lotions, tinctures, salves, pet bedding, and for almost any other purpose you can imagine. The fad of lavender has hyperbolized its powers. Is it effective for everything it is claimed to help? Probably not, but this hasn't slowed the utilization. Again, quality matters, and you will likely find a market for the highest-quality flowers. These should be flowers that have been harvested, sorted, and dried in only the best conditions, to assure that no molds or mildews, dust, or other contaminants have tainted the flowers. High oil content seems to be desirable as well, which makes fragrant varieties such as Tuscan™ particularly attractive. You can easily contact the healing arts professionals in your area who use herbs to let them know if you have a medicinal-grade product. Also, remember to price this grade accordingly—highest quality should bring the highest price. Veterinarians and beekeepers also use lavender for pest control.

Lavender Crafts

The possibilities of using lavender in fine handcrafts is as endless as the imagination. Traditional uses include sachets, wreaths, wands, oils, soaps, salves, lotions, baskets, bed pillows, soothing eye pillows, fragrant massage oils, flower arrangements, wedding corsages, and in more elaborate floral arrangements. Each year we discover and invent new uses for lavender, as will you.

Friends

Lavender attracts a wonderful group of animals. When the bloom is on, bumblebees, hummingbirds, honeybees, and butterflies are just a few who enhance the delight of our gardens. We love the gentle hum of the bees as they lift from flower to flower. People often want to know when the peak of the bloom is? It's simple: when the plants are covered with bumblebees.

Weddings

Create a beautiful lavender farm and young couples will beat a path to your door. Everyone is looking for a lovely place to celebrate marriage. Parking, bathrooms, changing rooms, and reception space are important also, but it can give you another way to have your farm be successful.

ARANTZ AND THE TRACTOR:

Our dear friend Kathryn Kelsey was a Peace Corps volunteer in Benin, Africa, when she was fresh out of college in the 1980s. While in Benin, she befriended an African family and became close to their young son, Arantz. Years later, Arantz came to visit the United States and to go to high school with Kathryn and her husband Chris, both of whom were teachers living in Seattle. It was an amazing year for all; one of the high points was when they came to stay at the farm for a few days. They came during the summer time, and one thing I like to do is give people, who otherwise might never have the experience, a chance to drive the tractor. Tractors can do a lot of work and they spark the imagination in ways that few objects do. In Benin, which is a very poor country, a tractor would be very significant to your status. Arantz was eager and a little nervous to drive the ours. The tractor was a 1940s Ford Ferguson 9N, about as classic a machine as exists in the world. Classic in tractor speak can also mean uncomfortable, hard to drive, and dangerous, all qualities easily overlooked in the romance of tractors. Tractors change people's lives, mostly for the better, but this little story might have turned out differently. With its solid metal seat, it took some doing for both Arantz and me to sit on the tractor. Disregarding the wise tractor taboo against having two drivers on the seat, we set off at low speed and in low gear, driving around the hills and fields of the farm. Once Arantz felt more comfortable, we became a little ambitious and started up the eastern flank of the property on a cat road that runs around the perimeter. I often ran this road with the tractor, and Arantz seemed at ease with the steering and breaking necessary to go as slowly as we were moving. All was well until we headed up a slight incline on the trail and the front wheel cut left, quickly taking us off the trail onto a slope where it was obvious we were going to roll the tractor on top of us. In a flash, I knew we were going to die; this would be the headline telling everyone how: "Stupid Nursery Owner Dies in Tractor Rollover Taking Life of Innocent Young African with Him." But we didn't roll over. The tractor settled into a precarious but balanced stop off the trail, and we jumped off in a second and started screaming in relief to be alive. Arantz shouted at the top of his lungs, "It was my grandfather, Joey, who saved us. He was here and he stopped the tractor from going over!" All I thought then, and all I think now when I see the rut where the tractor stopped is, "Thank you Arantz's grandfather!" (I have since gotten rid of the classic Ford 9N and now have a less classic but safer and four-wheel-drive Kubota with a seat belt, roll bar, and slightly more intelligent driver.)

ɞ

EQUIPMENT

I particularly enjoy writing this section of the book, because I laugh when I think of the equipment with which we started. Basically, we had nothing more specialized than the normal set of garden tools used for all-purpose gardening—things like shovels, hand pruners, and a wheelbarrow. Our first step forward was to build some propagation boxes modeled after the potato trays we saw in the movie, *The Crying Game*, as I described earlier. Next, we used an old, covered lawn pool as a greenhouse before the snow knocked it down. We actually did pretty well with this equipment, which once again goes to show that "the best piece of equipment is between your ears." Okay, we do have a few more things now, and if you want to scale up you'll need some other equipment, but most of it will be for the sake of convenience rather than out of necessity. Sure, we like to look at catalogs and dream, but we basically do not buy any equipment until we're sure we need it. Here are a few items, in no particular order, with an explanation for why we acquired them.

Greenhouse: It rains a lot in the Northwest. It's nice to be dry and a little warmer in the rainy seasons. Also, we can grow plants in pots without having the rain wash away the nutrition in the soil. We use steel and plastic hoop houses.

Rototiller: This is my personal favorite; it's handy for turning soil, adding soil amendments, and weeding rows. Ours is a Honda.

Trailer or pickup for transporting soil: We use a pickup, but we would like a detachable trailer.

Shed: A shed provides more covered space to store equipment and to work. In the Northwest you can't have too much covered space.

Pruners: Before I take Nancy's hand, I make sure she doesn't have these in hers. They are indispensable; just don't use cheap models, they'll only cause you grief (and tendonitis or carpel tunnel syndrome, or both).

Landscape cloth: This is for covering large areas where you don't want weeds. Our greenhouse ground is covered with it, as is the outside area where we grow plants in pots. It is better than plastic sheeting because it drains and breathes.

Propagation tables: Our 4-foot-wide tables span both sides of a 20'30' greenhouse. The tables are raised benches covered with soil, heated by subsurface circulated hot water. We can hold almost 200 plug trays at a time on these benches. These are what we fill with soil and place cuttings 1/cell in trays of 50/72/128/168 cells per tray.

Pots: Clearly, pots are standard fare for growing and selling plants; they are available new and recycled in a wide variety of shapes and sizes.

Storage bins for fertilizer: I like galvanized garbage cans.

Potting bench: This should be a stout bench for potting built to a comfortable standing height. Situate it where you can dump soil on it with your tractor's loader, where you can have shade in the heat, and where it can remain dry when it rains.

Shovels: Buy good ones!

Sprayer: We have one 4-gallon backpack sprayer. It's awkward to use but effective for fertilizing.

Watering supplies: Good hoses, hose shutoffs, wands, gated Y's, and sprinklers are essential. Think before you buy as cheap materials will make you cry.

ଔ

Afterward

While writing and revising this book I thought of many experiences that are part of the every day life of growing things. I tried to include as many of them as I could but there are too many to include them all. Fortunately, the things you discover as you work with plants, land, and the seasons will come to you as well. There simply is no way to tell everything that matters. I've worked with living things all my life: exotic animals, fish, oysters, plants and people, and if there's one thing I know: a lot is unpredictable. It is in human nature to plan and plan and plan, but in time, you discover that the unpredictable things and the mistakes are what bring you knowledge, joy, and inject a little mystery into your life. I hope anything I've omitted leads you only to small and wonderful mistakes. Good luck on your voyage, and may there always be some mystery to your life.

❧

General Index

ABOUT THE AUTHOR

Joseph Emil Blum was born in Ohio and raised in New York. His first paid job was removing ice from a Cadillac at the age of seven. Abandoning that promising career, he then went on to the care of exotic animals, life-guarding, home insulating, construction, carpentry, fisheries biology, teacher of the living and the dying, before an extended period of lavender farming and writing. At the age of nineteen he moved to the Pacific Northwest and now lives in rural Oregon. In 1992, he founded and directed the Lorane Film Society and later Lorane's Rural Arts Center, in the lovely town of Lorane, Oregon. In 2008, he published his first novel, *Bedtime Stories: Tales of a Cinematic Wanderer* and has numerous published essays, newspaper columns, poems, and stories.

josephemilblum.com

℅

7207928R00038

Printed in Great Britain
by Amazon.co.uk, Ltd.,
Marston Gate.